JOURNEY TO BEIJING 2008

Grades 4-6

10 9 8 7 6 5 4 3 2 1

ISBN   1-58000-126-2

TCR   2165

S0-ARD-454

DIRECTOR OF OPERATIONS	Robin L. Howland
PROJECT MANAGER	Bryan K. Howland
WRITERS	Greg Camden, M.A., and Eric Migliaccio
EDITOR	Mary S. Jones, M.A.
COVER DESIGNER	Kevin Barnes
ART COORDINATOR / ILLUSTRATOR	Renée Christine Yates
IMAGING	Rosa C. See

Published in association with
and distributed by:

Griffin Publishing LLC

P. O. Box 28627

Santa Ana, CA 92799-8627

www.griffinpublishing.com

Manufactured in the United States of America

Teacher Created Resources, Inc.

6421 Industry Way

Westminster, CA 92683

www.teachercreated.com

Table of Contents

Meeting Standards

The lessons in this book meet the following standards, which are used with permission from McREL.
Copyright 2006 McREL. Mid-continent Research for Education and Learning
2250 S. Parker Road, Suite 500, Aurora, CO 80014
Telephone: 303-337-0990 Website: *www.mcrel.org/standards-benchmarks*

Standards and Benchmarks

ART

Standard 1.	Understands connections among the various art forms and other disciplines

GEOGRAPHY

Standard 1.	Understands the characteristics and uses of maps, globes, and other geographic tools and technologies
Standard 10.	Understands the nature and complexity of Earth's cultural mosaics
Standard 14.	Understands how human actions modify the physical environment
Standard 15.	Understands how physical systems affect human systems
Standard 18.	Understands global development and environmental issues

HISTORY

Standard 7.	(K–4 History) Understands selected attributes and historical developments of societies in Africa, the Americas, Asia, and Europe
Standard 1.	(Historical Understanding) Understands and knows how to analyze chronological relationships and patterns
Standard 14.	(World History) Understands major developments in East Asia and Southeast Asia in the era of the Tang Dynasty from 600 to 900 CE
Standard 19.	(World History) Understands the maturation of an interregional system of communication, trade, and cultural exchange during a period of Chinese economic power and Islamic expansion

LANGUAGE ARTS

Standard 1.	Uses the general skills and strategies of the writing process
Standard 4.	Gathers and uses information for research purposes
Standard 5.	Uses the general skills and strategies of the reading process
Standard 7.	Uses reading skills and strategies to understand and interpret a variety of informational texts

LIFE SKILLS

Standard 1.	Understands and applies the basic principles of presenting an argument
Standard 3.	Effectively uses mental processes that are based on identifying similarities and differences

MATHEMATICS

Standard 1.	Uses a variety of strategies in the problem-solving process
Standard 2.	Understands and applies basic and advanced properties of the concepts of numbers
Standard 3.	Uses basic and advanced procedures while performing the processes of computation
Standard 9.	Understands the general nature and uses of mathematics

SCIENCE

Standard 10.	Understands forces and motion

The Beijing 2008 Olympic Games

The weather is heating up, and soon the excitement will be, too. After four long years, the time for the Summer Olympic Games has come again. The world's greatest athletes are making their last-minute travel arrangements, and you will be right there with them. Your destination: the Far East. Your journey to the 2008 Olympic Games in Beijing, China, begins here!

This is an exciting time, not just for the athletes but also for all who are involved in this historical event. Imagine you are a member of the media, packing for your trip halfway across the world. It will be your job to take in the sights and sounds of the Olympic Games and report them to the people back home. What examples of Chinese culture will you experience? What great feats of athleticism will you witness? Who will be the latest in the long line of Olympic heroes?

Before you embark for Beijing, think about what you already know about China and the Olympic Games. Then consider what you hope to learn during your Olympic experience. Fill in the chart below. Here are some ideas to think about:

- foods of China
- customs of China
- history/geography of China

- events in the Olympic Games
- what is needed for the Olympic Games
- who competes in the Olympic Games

What I Know About China	**What I Hope to Learn About China**
What I Know About the Olympic Games	**What I Hope to Learn About the Olympic Games**

Olympic Vocabulary

When you are going to visit a new country or a different culture, it is always a good idea to know a few words from that country's language. As you travel through this book on your way to China and the Beijing 2008 Olympic Games, you will come across a few words over and over again. Here's a handy guide:

BCE — "Before the Current (or Common) Era"; the time period from the beginning of time until the year 1 BCE

CE — "The Current (or Common) Era"; the time period from 1 CE to the present time

disciplines — sub-categories of a sport

dynasty — when people from the same family rule a country over a long time period

modern — relating to the present time or recent times

renewable — of an energy source that can be used again

truce — an agreement to be peaceful

venue — a place where an organized event happens

Part I: Use your new words to fill in the blanks and complete these sentences.

1. The music concert will be held in the new _____ that was built last year.

2. The Declaration of Independence was signed in the year 1776 _____ .

3. Swimming and diving are _____ of the sport known as aquatics.

4. Grandpa Jim says that reality TV is the worst invention of _____ times.

5. Mom made Bobby and me sign a _____ and agree to stop fighting.

Part II: Draw lines to connect each of the vocabulary words to the idea it best matches.

6. truce   **A.** water, wind, and solar power

7. dynasty   **B.** something that's happening now

8. renewable   **C.** something that ends a war

9. modern   **D.** a family that runs a country

10. BCE   **E.** the time that was many thousands of years ago

The Ancient Olympic Games

Before you travel across the world to the Beijing 2008 Olympic Games, it is important to first travel back in time to the year it all began. You'll have to travel way back, exactly 2,784 years ago to find the first Olympics. Back in 776 BCE, the Games did not look too much like the global event you see today. For instance, there was only one event back then! It was called the *stadion*, and it was a running race that covered a distance of 180–240 meters (about 200–260 yards). By comparison, the Beijing 2008 Olympic Games will feature 302 events.

Here is a list of things that describe either the Ancient Olympic Games or the Beijing 2008 Olympic Games. See if you can match each description with its correct time period. Write the letter of each description inside or next to the pictures of the athletes to the left.

Ancient Olympic Games

Beijing 2008 Olympic Games

A – ceremonies begin in 776 BCE

B – ceremonies begin on 8/8/08

C – athletes from 202 countries compete

D – BMX bike racing first introduced

E – boxers sometimes put metal in their hard leather gloves

F – only free men who speak Greek can compete

G – 302 total events

H – chariot racing first introduced

I – winners receive an olive branch and much honor

J – athletes wear highly advanced clothing and equipment

K – outlawed by Roman Emperor Theodosius I in 393 CE

L – women compete in 127 events

M – winners receive a gold medal and much honor

N – athletes wear very little clothing

Truth or Myth?

The further you go back in history, the more difficult it is to know if the stories we hear are truth (they did happen that way) or myth (they didn't quite happen that way, or they didn't even happen at all!). These days, when something happens, it is often caught on film and shown on television or the Internet within hours. Back in the time of the Ancient Olympic Games, no such technology existed. We have to rely on the tales that have been passed down through the generations.

Here are some stories about the tremendous athletes whose Olympic feats are legendary:

- **Milo of Kroton**

  This wrestler won six Olympic competitions. He was known for his strong wrists and hands. It was said that he would show his strength by holding out his hands with his fingers spread out. No man could even bend his little finger.

- **Melankomas of Caria**

  This boxer was known for his handsome body and good looks. His boxing style was to spend the entire fight avoiding the blows of his opponents. He wouldn't throw any punches himself! He was so quick that no one ever hit him. His opponents got so tired and frustrated that they gave up.

- **Astylos of Croton**

  This Olympic hero won running events in three straight Olympic Games. He became a hated man, though, when he accepted money to compete for a different city than his hometown of Croton. The citizens of Croton kicked him out of their city and destroyed the statue of him that once stood there.

- **Cynisca of Sparta**

  She is the answer to the trivia question: Who was the first woman to win an Olympic medal? Women were not allowed to compete back then, but they were allowed to own horses. And when a horse won an equestrian event, it wasn't the rider who was given the medal, it was the owner of the horse.

Activity: Imagine that there was no way to film or record the athletes or celebrities of today. People would have to tell stories about them so that future generations would remember them. On a separate piece of paper, write a story or myth about an athlete or celebrity from today. Have fun exaggerating their skills or beauty. What amazing feats did your famous person accomplish? Why should this person be remembered for thousands of years?

Another Idea: When you write your story or myth, don't give the name of the athlete or celebrity you are writing about. Exchange stories with your classmates and see if they can name the person being described.

The Modern Olympic Games

During the 19th century, archaeologists began to excavate the ruins of Olympia, a city in Greece that had been buried by an earthquake over 1,000 years before. It was then that many clues were discovered about the Ancient Olympic Games that used to be held there. A French teacher and historian named Pierre de Coubertin took an interest in these findings. He wanted to get the youth of the world competing in sports instead of fighting in wars. He felt that a modern version of the Olympic Games was a way to accomplish these goals.

In 1894 de Coubertin founded the International Olympic Committee (IOC). The committee met and decided to put his plan into action. They also decided to begin this new Olympic tradition in 1896 in Greece, the country where it all began. At the time, there was a great debate in the IOC. Some argued that the Olympic Games should always be played in Greece. But de Coubertin was one who believed that the Games should be hosted by different countries throughout the world. This idea gave many countries a chance to see this international event up close.

Pierre de Coubertin

The 1896 Olympic Games were held in Athens, Greece, from April 6 to April 15. Athletes from 14 nations competed in just nine sports: athletics (track and field), cycling, fencing, gymnastics, shooting, swimming, tennis, weightlifting, and wrestling. Here are some of the highlights of the 1896 Games:

- A Greek athlete named Spyridon Louis became a national hero when he won the marathon race.

- Brothers John Paine and Sumner Paine became the first relatives to come in first place in Olympic events when they each won a shooting event.

- A Greek athlete named Stamata Revithi was told that she could not compete in the Games because she was a woman. As a sign of protest, she ran a complete marathon course the day after the men had.

Many things have changed in the 112 years since those first Modern Olympic Games. Now over 11,000 men and women from over 200 nations compete in 28 different sports. In 1896, the first- and second-place finishers received silver medals; it wasn't until 1904 that the gold medal was awarded for first place, a silver medal for second place, and a bronze medal for third place. Other symbols of the Olympic Games—such as the torch and the Olympic rings—have been introduced, too.

The Modern Games Challenge

Use the information from The Modern Olympic Games on page 8 to complete these activities.

Part I

Directions: Put these events in time order. Write a "1" by the event that happened first in history and a "5" by the event that happened last.

_____ The bronze medal was given to athletes who finished in third place.

_____ An earthquake destroyed Olympia, Greece.

_____ Over 11,000 athletes took part in an Olympic Games.

_____ Pierre de Coubertin started the International Olympic Committee.

_____ Spyridon Louis won the first marathon race in the Modern Olympic Games.

Part II

Directions: Fill in the circle next to each correct answer.

1. What is another word for *excavate*?

   (a) dig   (b) discover   (c) clean

2. How many years passed between the first Modern Olympic Games and the Beijing 2008 Olympic Games?

   (a) 1,000   (b) 28   (c) 112

3. Which word is an example of a compound word?

   (a) weightlifting   (b) committee   (c) national

4. How many more sports will be played in the 2008 Olympic Games than were played in the 1896 Olympic Games?

   (a) 28   (b) 19   (c) 29

5. Which is the correct way to spell the word for the people who study ancient ruins?

   (a) archaologists   (b) archaelogists   (c) archaeologists

6. The Beijing 2008 Olympic Games are also known as the "Games of the XXIX Olympiad." What number do the Roman numerals XXIX stand for?

   (a) 28   (b) 19   (c) 29

7. Challenge: How many years passed between the beginning of the Ancient Olympic Games in 776 BCE and the beginning of the Modern Olympic Games in 1896 CE?

   (a) 2,672 years   (b) 1,120 years   (c) 1,020 years

Olympic Host Cities—Summer

Year	Host City	Host Country
1896	Athens	Greece
1900	Paris	France
1904	St. Louis, MO	United States
1908	London	England
1912	Stockholm	Sweden
1920	Antwerp	Belgium
1924	Paris	France
1928	Amsterdam	The Netherlands
1932	Los Angeles, CA	United States
1936	Berlin	Germany
1948	London	England
1952	Helsinki	Finland
1956	Melbourne	Australia
1960	Rome	Italy
1964	Tokyo	Japan
1968	Mexico City	Mexico
1972	Munich	Germany
1976	Montreal	Canada
1980	Moscow	Soviet Union (USSR)
1984	Los Angeles, CA	United States
1988	Seoul	South Korea
1992	Barcelona	Spain
1996	Atlanta, GA	United States
2000	Sydney	Australia
2004	Athens	Greece
2008	Beijing	China
2012	London	England

The Host Cities Challenge

Use your list of Summer Olympic Host Cities on page 10 to answer the following questions.

1. Name the city and country that hosted the Olympic Games in 1972.

   _____

2. Which four cities have hosted the Olympic Games at least twice?

   _____

   _____

3. Complete the bar graph below to show how many times each country has hosted the Olympic Games. (Not all host countries are listed.) Fill in the correct number of bars for each country.

Host Countries Graph

	1	2	3	4	5
Australia					
Canada					
China					
France					
Germany					
Greece					
Italy					
Mexico					
United States					
U.S.S.R.					

4. How many times has the Olympic Games been hosted by a North-American city? Circle the correct number and write the cities on the lines.

   4   6   8

   _____

   _____

   _____

5. What was the most number of years between Olympic Games? _____

   Between which years was this gap? _____

   Why were there so many years between Olympic Games during this time? Use an encyclopedia or the Internet to find out. Write your answer here.

   _____

   _____

Being a Good Host

It takes more than sunny skies and a few swimming pools to host an Olympic Games. Think about the things a smoothly-run Olympic Games would need, and consider the ways a city could be prepared or unprepared to provide those needs. Fill out the chart with as many details as you can think of.

	Why This Is Needed	Well Prepared	Not Prepared
Housing			
Stadiums/Venues			
Transportation			
Volunteers			

Now that you have thought about what makes a good host city for the Olympic Games, answer the following questions:

- Would your city be a good host for the Olympic Games? _____

- Explain your answer. _____

  _____

- Would it be a better host for the Olympic Winter Games? _____

- Explain your answer. _____

  _____

To see how Beijing is preparing for the 2008 Olympic Games,
visit the official website at *http://en.beijing2008.cn.*

Welcome to Beijing, China!

"Good afternoon, ladies and gentlemen. This is your flight captain speaking. In just a short while, we will be landing in Beijing Capital International Airport. Beijing is a northern city in the People's Republic of China, and it is also the country's capital. In fact, the word 'Beijing' means 'Northern Capital.'

"More people call China home than any other country in the world. Over 1.3 billion people live in this Asian country, and over 15 million of those people live in Beijing. Add to that number the tens of thousands of athletes, spectators, and media members buzzing in and around the city for the Olympic Games, and you can see that Beijing will be a busy beehive of activity for the next few weeks.

"During your stay, you are encouraged to soak up the local flavor and rich history of this country and its people. Observe the customs, sample the food, and visit a few of China's many historical sites. Hike along the Great Wall or take a stroll through Tiananmen Square. The Olympic Games are not just about sports and the athletes who compete in them; they are also about the meeting of many cultures and peoples.

"Currently, the temperature on the ground in Beijing is 34 degrees. Remember that's 34 degrees Celsius, which equals about 93 degrees Fahrenheit, so I hope you all brought sunscreen.

"Before we land, please fill out the form below. As one of the lucky people here to witness the Games in person, what places or events are you most looking forward to seeing? Write your top three."

Bei Jing Huan Ying Ni

("Welcome to Beijing")

Things I Hope to Do and See in Beijing

1. _____

_____

2. _____

_____

3. _____

_____

The Geography of China

Learn more about the cities of China and about the seas and islands that surround this fascinating country. Then, cut out the map labels and paste them into the correct spaces on the map of China on page 15. Use an atlas or the Internet to help you.

Map Labels	Things to Know
Beijing	Once known as Peking, the northern city of Beijing is the capital of China and also its second most populated city. Of the 37 venues where Olympic events will be held, 31 of them will be in Beijing.
Shanghai	The port city of Shanghai is the most populated city in China and the ninth most populated city in the world. No port in the world sees more cargo (443 million tons per year) pass through it than Shanghai.
Tibet	This South Asian region is controlled by China, though many feel that it should be a free and separate country. Tibet has the highest average elevation on Earth, and it's often called "The Roof of the World."
Mongolia	This region is bordered to the south by China and to the north by Russia. Because of its harsh climate, Mongolia is the least densely populated independent country in the world. It is landlocked, meaning it is completely bordered by land and not connected to any ocean or sea.
Hong Kong	Hong Kong is an island group that is located in the South China Sea. Britain ruled this region from 1842 until 1997 when it was transferred to Chinese rule. Hong Kong will host equestrian events during the Beijing 2008 Olympic Games.
Taiwan	Taiwan is an island off the Eastern coast of China. In 1945, after being defeated in World War II, Japan surrendered control of this island to China.
Pacific Ocean	The Pacific Ocean is the largest of Earth's ocean areas. It extends from the Arctic in the north to the Antarctic in the south, and it has Asia and Australia as its western border and the Americas as its eastern border.
South China Sea	The South China Sea is part of the Pacific Ocean. It is the sixth largest body of water in the world.

The Map of China

Paste the labels from page 14 in the appropriate place on the map of China below.

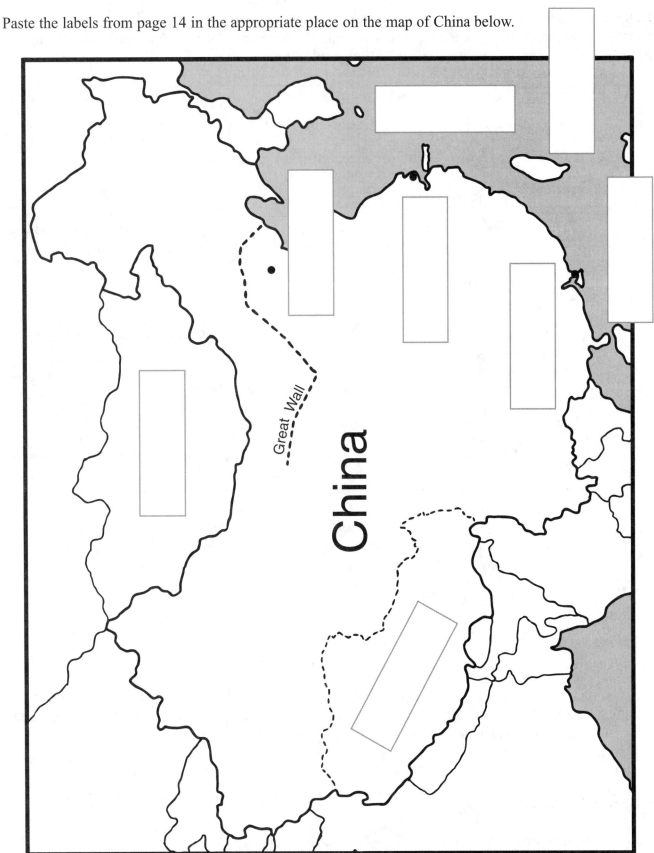

Great Wall

China

Beijing Time Line

A city as old as Beijing has seen a lot of change throughout its years—different rulers, different city limits, even different names. Below is a time line of the various events that have shaped the Beijing that will be on display during the Beijing 2008 Olympic Games.

The Current Era (CE)

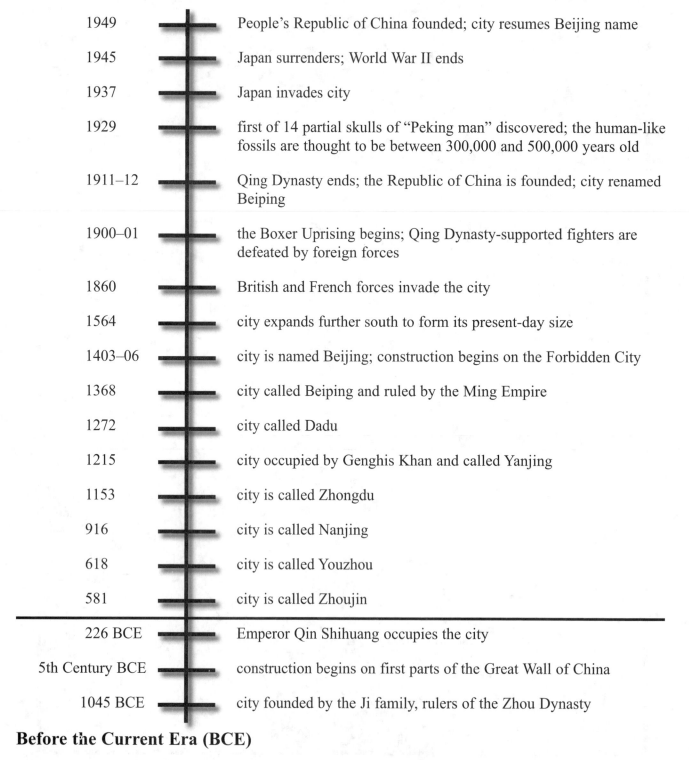

1949	People's Republic of China founded; city resumes Beijing name
1945	Japan surrenders; World War II ends
1937	Japan invades city
1929	first of 14 partial skulls of "Peking man" discovered; the human-like fossils are thought to be between 300,000 and 500,000 years old
1911–12	Qing Dynasty ends; the Republic of China is founded; city renamed Beiping
1900–01	the Boxer Uprising begins; Qing Dynasty-supported fighters are defeated by foreign forces
1860	British and French forces invade the city
1564	city expands further south to form its present-day size
1403–06	city is named Beijing; construction begins on the Forbidden City
1368	city called Beiping and ruled by the Ming Empire
1272	city called Dadu
1215	city occupied by Genghis Khan and called Yanjing
1153	city is called Zhongdu
916	city is called Nanjing
618	city is called Youzhou
581	city is called Zhoujin
226 BCE	Emperor Qin Shihuang occupies the city
5th Century BCE	construction begins on first parts of the Great Wall of China
1045 BCE	city founded by the Ji family, rulers of the Zhou Dynasty

Before the Current Era (BCE)

Dynasty Match

Many of the periods of Chinese history are named after the ruling families, or dynasties, of the time. Use the clues below to find out when five of China's most important dynasties ruled. Place a checkmark in the correct boxes to match the dynasties to their years of rule.

- The Tang Dynasty ruled during the 8th Century CE.
- The Han Dynasty ruled during the period when the Common Era (CE) began.
- The Qing Dynasty began in the year that the Ming Dynasty ended.

	Tang Dynasty	Han Dynasty	Zhou Dynasty	Qing Dynasty	Ming Dynasty
1122 BCE – 256 BCE					
206 BCE – 220 CE					
618 CE – 907 CE					
1368 CE – 1644 CE					
1644 CE – 1911 CE					

Use your answers from the chart above to find out when certain important events happened and which dynasty was ruling China at the time. Write the name of the dynasty on the line. The first one has been done for you.

__Ming__ 1. Construction began on the Forbidden City in 1403 CE.

_____ 2. The Silk Road, which connected China to the West was reopened in 639 CE. Trade between the two regions thrived.

_____ 3. Kong Fuzi (also known as Confucius) lived from 551–479 BCE.

_____ 4. By reigning for 61 years (from 1662–1722 CE) Kangxi had the longest reign of any Emperor of China.

_____ 5. The modern papermaking process was invented around the turn of the 1st Century CE.

_____ 6. The Great Wall was expanded and reinforced after the emperor was captured by Mongolians in 1449 CE.

_____ 7. The Giant Wild Goose Pagoda was built in 652 CE, and it is now a famous Chinese landmark.

_____ 8. This dynasty was hurt badly by supporting the Boxer Uprising of 1900. The Boxers were defeated by a group of eight nations.

_____ 9. China's most famous historian, Sima Qian, died in 90 BCE.

_____ 10. The Ancient Olympic Games began in Greece in 776 CE.

Sights to See

The city of Beijing is filled with fascinating sights that can't be seen anywhere else in the world. While visiting for the Olympic Games, athletes and spectators will be sure to take advantage of this once-in-a-lifetime experience in a city that has been around for thousands of years. Here are a few of those can't-miss sights:

The Great Wall

At over 4,000 miles (6,400 km) long, the Great Wall of China is the longest human-made structure in the world. This wall of stone, earth, and bricks was mostly built and rebuilt during the 5th century BCE and the 16th century CE. It was made to protect the northern borders of the Chinese Empire.

The sections of the wall near Beijing are among China's most popular tourist destinations. People come from around the world to climb the steps of this ancient structure. In July of 2007, the Great Wall of China was chosen as one of the "New Seven Wonders of the World."

The Forbidden City

Located in the middle of Beijing, the Forbidden City was once the imperial palace of the ruling dynasties. Built in the 15th century, this "city" within Beijing is made up of nearly 1,000 buildings. It is the world's largest surviving palace complex.

The Forbidden City is surrounded by walls and a moat (a deep, wide, water-filled ditch), and it is contained inside a large area known as the Imperial City. The Imperial City itself is enclosed in an area known as the Inner City. The Outer City is to the south.

One of the main tourist destinations inside the Forbidden City is the Palace Museum, which holds over one million artifacts and works of art.

Discussion Questions

- The Great Wall of China was chosen as one of the New Seven Wonders of the World. If you were put in charge of making the list, which seven manmade or natural wonders would you choose? (To see the actual list, visit *http://www.new7wonders.com* and click the "results" link.)

- A controversy was sparked when a popular American coffee franchise opened a store outside the Palace Museum in The Forbidden City in 2000. (It was closed in July of 2007.) Many Chinese citizens felt this was an insult to the culture and history of the Forbidden City. What is your opinion? Which do you feel is more important: updating places to meet the popular tastes of the day or respecting tradition and keeping ancient landmarks free of signs of the modern world?

Travel Brochure

Imagine that you and your classmates have been put in charge of tourism for the Beijing 2008 Olympic Games. Design a travel brochure to advertise one of the many fascinating tourist destinations in and around the city. Choose one of the following:

- Tiananmen Square
- The Summer Palace
- The Temple of Heaven
- The Altar of Earth

- Lugouqiao (Marco Polo) Bridge
- The World Park in Beijing
- The China Millennium Monument
- The Ruins of Yuanmingyuan
  (the Garden of Perfection and Brightness)

Use an encyclopedia or the Internet to research your chosen sight. Include pictures (either drawn, printed from the Internet, or cut from a magazine) that will make people want to visit the place. Make the cover attractive and colorful. On the inside of your brochure, include information about the history of the place. Why was it built? What happened there? Why should people come visit?

Use these materials and follow the instructions below to make your brochure:

Materials

- variety of heavy 8 1/2" x 11" paper
  (white or colored)
- construction paper
- markers
- ruler
- scissors
- glue
- pictures (from magazines or
  printed from the Internet)

Instructions

1. Take one piece of heavy paper for your brochure. Turn the paper horizontally so that it is longest from left to right.

2. Fold left 1/3 of paper forward towards the middle.

3. Fold right 1/3 of paper backward towards the middle.

4. Now that you have your brochure, begin writing, drawing, and pasting pictures on it. Create pictures by cutting them from magazines, drawing, and/or using construction paper.

The Silk Road

Legend has it that a 14-year-old Chinese empress discovered silk in the 27th century BCE when a fluffy white ball fell into her cup of tea as she walked under a mulberry tree. That fluffy white ball was the cocoon of the silkworm, and the fibers it produced played an important role in the growth of civilization. The silk cloth that was made from those cocoons was a luxury item that everyone wanted. For 3,000 years, though, China kept the silk-making process a secret from the rest of the world. (And for those who thought of selling that secret or giving it away, the punishment was death.) For China, the silk business made them trade partners with everyone from Egypt to India to the Roman Empire. The route along which those trades were made was called the Silk Road. And more than silk was exchanged on this road; culture, art, and experience were also passed from one group of people to another. This may not have happened for hundreds of years if it weren't for the work of the silkworm.

Eventually, the Silk Road began to show signs of failing. Other Asian cultures learned of the process and began making their own silk. The Roman emperors, worried by how much of their wealth was being sent to China for silk, took steps to stop trade along the route. In addition, using the Silk Road became a highly dangerous journey as different groups set up their homes along the route. These groups were not always at peace with China, and merchants traveling along the route were attacked. Then, in 552 CE, the Roman emperor Justinian I sent two monks to India where they stole a small number of silk-moth eggs. This led to a thriving silk industry in the Roman Empire.

The Silk Road lay unused for many years, until an explorer named Marco Polo traveled the route to China in the late 13th century CE. Even when the Silk Road wasn't being used, nations from the West were looking for ways to trade with China. It is even said that Christopher Columbus was looking for a new Silk Road when he sailed west in 1492. Instead, he discovered the Americas.

Map of the Silk Road Route

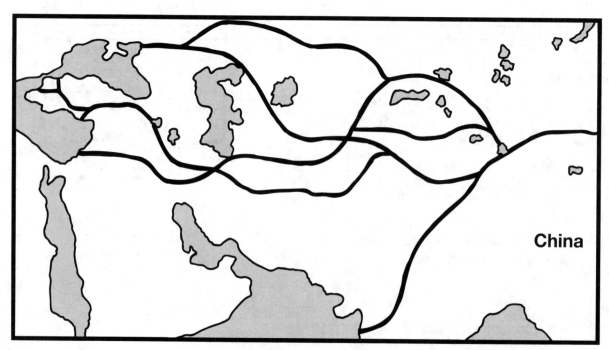

China

Making Silk

Follow the road below to find out the secret the Chinese kept for so long—how a worm can make such a beautiful fabric. Use the words along the side of the road to fill in the blanks you encounter on your journey.

Step 1
Silk moths lay _ _ _◯ on a special kind of paper.

Step 2
The eggs hatch and out come silkworm _ _◯_ _ _ _ _◯_, which feed on fresh mulberry leaves

Step 3
After more than a month of _ _ _◯_ _, the silkworms are 10,000 times heavier than they once were.

caterpillars

cocoons

destroying

eating

eggs

liquid

mile

moths

Step 5
The worms produce _ _◯_ _ silk, which they shoot out of tiny holes in their heads. This substance turns solid when it hits the air.

Step 4
The silkworms move their heads back and forth as they begin spinning their _ _◯_ _ _ _.

Step 6
Within a few days, the silkworm will have spun one _ _◯_ of silk fibers. It will be completely surrounded by its cocoon.

Step 7
At this point, the cocoons are heated and most of the silkworms are killed. This is to keep them from turning into _ _◯_ _ and _ _ _ _◯_ _ _ _ their cocoons as they leave them.

Bonus:
Look at the circled letters you've collected along the road. Place them below in the order that you collected them, and they will spell out the name given to the practice of raising silkworms.

Step 8
Only a few worms are allowed to turn into moths. Those moths go on to lay eggs of their own.

__ __ __ __ __ __ __ __ u __ e

An Important Plant

Did you know that, with the exception of water, more tea is drunk worldwide than any other beverage? And in no country has tea played a more important role than it has in China. Even today, it continues to be the basis for many customs and practices.

There are several myths about the origins of this beverage. In one of the most popular, tea is said to have been discovered accidentally by Emperor Shennong in 2737 BCE. The story tells that he liked to have his drinking water boiled to ensure that it was clean, and one day a leaf from a wild tea bush fell into the boiling water. The emperor drank it and found it to his liking; and so, China's love of tea began. In the thousands of years that have followed, the Chinese have enjoyed tea for its flavor and for its medicinal qualities. It is good for digestion, full of vitamins, and it is also thought to bring relaxation to those who drink it.

This much-loved drink usually comes from the leaves of the *Camellia Sinensis* plant, though other plants and flowers are often added for flavoring and other benefits. Tea is made through a long and delicate process where young tea leaves are picked, heated, dried, and sifted. The flavor of the tea depends on the way it has been prepared.

There are many different types of tea, but there are four most basic categories:

- white tea (non-oxidized)
- green tea (slightly-oxidized)
- oolong tea (semi-oxidized)
- black/red tea (fully-oxidized).

These types are determined by the processes used to make them. As soon as tea leaves are picked, they begin to wilt and oxidize (or change on a molecular level). One way they change is by growing darker as the chlorophyll in the leaves breaks down. This process can be stopped by heating the leaves. So white tea is brewed quickly before this process begins—and so on, all the way to black tea, which is dried until the leaves have become fully oxidized.

While tea is drunk daily in China, it also has a special place in certain Chinese customs. It is prepared and consumed for many reasons, including to show respect and to pass on traditions from older generations to the younger members of the family. Tea also plays an important role in Chinese wedding ceremonies.

Tea Time

Choose one of the ideas below to show tea's role in the history and daily life of the people in China and around the world.

- Use an encyclopedia or the Internet to research your subject.
- Complete a report on your findings.
- Your report can be a visual aid (poster, diagram, chart, or graph), or it can include pictures and drawings that illustrate the written material.

The History of Tea

Tea was discovered over 4,700 years ago, so it has been through a lot in that time! Create a time line of the history of tea, from its discovery in China to the inventions of decaffeinated tea and the teabag.

Science of Tea

Describe the chemical processes that tea leaves go through from the moment they are picked off the plant until they are packaged for brewing. Write about the different types of tea leaves and create a chart or diagram showing the difference between each.

Language of Tea

Create a dictionary of words associated with tea. Include at least 15 words, and draw or print out pictures of as many as possible. Define lesser-known words, such as *chai, gaiwan,* and *tannins.* Provide the part of speech and pronunciation of each word.

Tea and Ceremony

Write about Chinese customs and ceremonies that involve tea. Describe the important role tea plays in daily life and in the traditional Chinese marriage ceremony.

Health Benefits of Tea

For over four thousand years, people have consumed tea for its health benefits, as well as its taste. Name at least five possible health benefits of tea consumption and give details about each.

Tea Taste Test

Do a taste test of each of the types of tea (white, green, oolong, black/red). Write a review of each. Which did you like most or least? Why? Be sure to include the brand names, countries of origin, and flavors of each type you tasted.

Variations for teachers:

- Assemble the reports into a class book about tea.
- Turn these reports into presentations in front of the class. Ask that students include a visual aid to show as they speak.

Calligraphy

The art of calligraphy is a highly-respected form of writing used in such Asian countries as China, Japan, and Korea. One who masters calligraphy must combine the creativity of an artist with the technical skill of a craftsman. The use of calligraphy in China dates back thousands of years, and at times it has been considered as the highest and purest form of painting. In fact, original writings by famous Chinese calligraphers are worth a great deal of money and are often hung on walls, just like paintings.

There are four basic tools that are needed to practice calligraphy. They are paper, ink, brush, and ink stone. Together, they are known as the Four Treasures of the Study.

Paper	Ink
A special paper called *xuanzhi* is the preferred type of paper to use. It is made from a specific plant, along with other materials like rice, bamboo, hemp, and mulberry. 	Calligraphy ink is traditionally black in color and it comes in sticks. The sticks must be rubbed with water on an ink stone until an ink of the right consistency is produced. 
Brush	**Ink Stone**
Brush handles can be made of bamboo or more expensive materials like ivory, silver, or gold. The hairs of the brush can be made from the hair or feathers of such animals as rabbits, deer, tigers, ducks, and wolves. The brush should be gripped between the thumb and middle finger and held straight up and down. The index finger lightly holds the brush in place, while the remaining two fingers are tucked under. 	The ink stone is made of stone or ceramics, and it is used to rub the solid ink stick. Once the ink is in liquid form, it is contained inside the ink stone. Learning to rub the ink correctly is considered to be an important part of being a calligrapher. 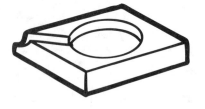

The Eight Principles of *Yong*

Years of dedicated practice are needed to master this ancient art. One of the best ways to practice is to write the Chinese character *yong* (see bottom right) over and over again. That is because this character contains the eight most basic strokes needed by calligraphers. It is thought that those who can write the *yong* character beautifully will be able to write all other characters with beauty, as well.

The word *yong* means "permanence" or "eternity." Complete the exercise on page 25 and see how long it takes you to master this important Chinese character.

永

The Eight Principles

Practice using the eight principal strokes of calligraphy to write the yong character.

1. "Sideway" or "Dot" (*a dot from top left to bottom right*)

2. "Bridle" or "Horizontal" (*a horizontal line*)

3. "Crossbow" or "Iron Pillar" (*a vertical line*)

4. "Leaping" or "Hook" (*a hook to the left*)

5. "Horsewhip" or "The Tiger's Tooth" (*a horizontal line that tapers to the upper right*)

6. "Slant" or "The Horn of Rhinoceros" (*a long, curving line that tapers to the lower left*)

7. "Short Slant" or "Bird Pecking" (*a short line tapering toward the lower left*)

8. "Wave" or "Pressing Forcefully" (*a line that thickens toward the lower right*)

Now try writing the yong character on your own.

Scrambled Inventions

The Ancient Chinese invented many things that are still a part of our lives today. See if you can unscramble the names of the inventions below. Use the descriptions to help you. (Hint: the first letter of each unscrambled word is underlined.)

Scrambled Word	Description	Name the Invention!
1. ilks	For centuries, only the Chinese knew how to make this luxury material from the cocoon of a caterpillar that feeds on mulberry leaves.	
2. chocktisps	These have been used throughout East Asia for thousands of years. It is rude to point with them or leave them sticking up in a bowl.	
3. teki	This was invented about 2,800 years ago and was first made of silk and bamboo. It was used for such things as measuring distances and testing the wind.	
4. reppa	In 105 CE, a civil servant named Cai Lun invented this by boiling, mashing, and pounding silk rags, mulberry bark, bamboo, and hemp.	
5. skewforri	These displays of light and sound date back to 12th century China. Their loud sounds were thought to frighten away evil spirits.	
6. spamsoc	The earliest mention of this magnetic device describes an iron "south-pointing fish" floating in a bowl of water and aligning itself to the south.	
7. trigpnin	This was created during the Tang Dynasty by an artisan who carved a wooden block into the form of a Chinese symbol and pressed it in ink, then on paper.	
8. pugwonder	Back in the 9th century, Chinese chemists came up with this explosive and deadly recipe while trying to make a potion that would give one eternal (everlasting) life!	
9. sigramphose	In 132 CE, Zhang Heng invented this instrument that used a pendulum and a series of levers to measure the vibration of the Earth when it shook.	
10. ascuba	Long before calculators existed, people used this hand-held item made of rods and disks to do mathematics calculations. Some in China still use it today.	

Chinese Math Puzzles

Magic Squares

These figures can be found all throughout history and in different cultures. A Chinese legend that dates back to at least 650 BCE tells the tale of a great flood on the river Lo. The people who lived nearby offered sacrifices to the river god to calm his anger and stop the flood. At that time, a turtle emerged from the floodwaters. On its shell was an arrangement of the numbers 1 through 9 in a 3 x 3 grid. Each row, column, and diagonal of the pattern added up to the number 15 (which is the number of days in each of the cycles of the Chinese solar year). This pattern came to be known as the Lo Shu square. "Lo Shu" means "scroll of the river Lo."

See if you can fill in the numbers to make this square. The middle number (5) has been given to you. Remember that each column, row, and diagonal must add up to 15, and you can only use each number from 1–9 once.

Hint: There is more than one possible pattern, but the Lo Shu square always has a "2" in the upper right-hand box and a "1" in the bottom middle box.

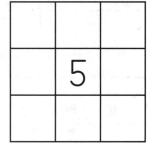

Yang Hui's Triangle

This famous geometric arrangement of numbers is often called Pascal's Triangle, but Yang Hui illustrated it in 1261 CE, over 350 years before the French mathematician Blaise Pascal was born. (And even before Yang Hui, a Chinese mathematician named Jia Xian is said to have discovered it sometime around 1100 CE.) Yang Hui's Triangle is useful because of the many complex mathematical patterns it forms.

Here's how it works:

- At the peak of the triangle is the number 1.
- Each number below is calculated by adding the two numbers directly above it.
- If there is no number above it to either side, then just add 0.

Here are the first nine rows of Yang Hui's Triangle. Use the formula described above to fill in the missing numbers.

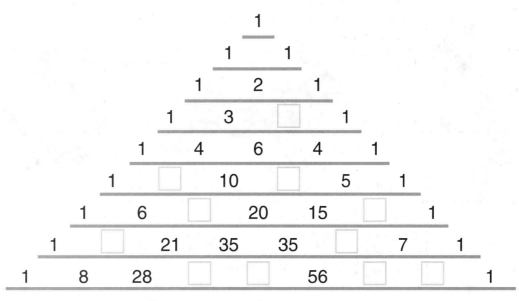

Chinese Tangrams

An old Chinese legend states that one day a servant of a Chinese emperor was carrying a very fragile, very expensive square-shaped piece of ceramic tile. On his way to the emperor, the servant stumbled. The tile fell to the ground and shattered into seven pieces. The servant was frantic as he tried to put the pieces back into the tile's square shape. He could not do it, but he did see that the pieces could be used to form many other shapes.

While we don't know if this legend is true, we do know that the famous puzzle known as the tangram originated in China. It is a puzzle made of seven pieces, called *tans*. Fit together in just the right way, the pieces form a perfect square. Fit together in other ways, they can take the form of hundreds of unique shapes and objects.

Tangram puzzles were brought from China to America in the early 1800s. They were once made from such materials as stone, bone, or clay, but are now more likely made from plastic or wood.

Activity: Can you solve the puzzles that have fascinated people for hundreds of years? Take a good look at the shapes below. Then use the *tans* on page 29 to create each shape.

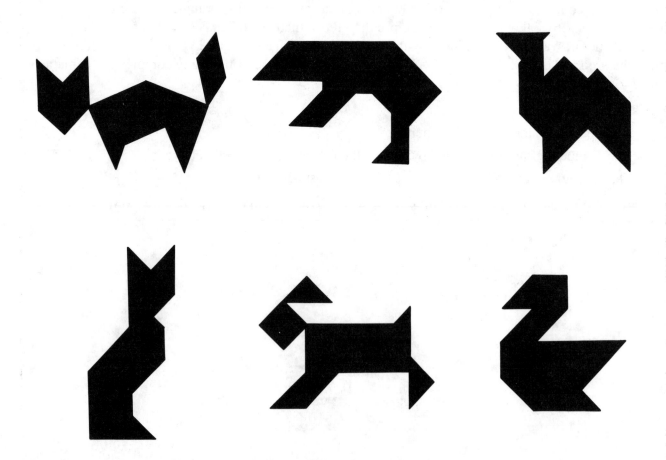

Bonus: Try to stump your classmates. Use the seven *tans* to make a shape, then draw it on the back of your paper. See if your friends can recreate your tangram.

Chinese Tangrams *(cont.)*

Cut out the seven shapes below and use them to form the tangrams on page 28.

Teacher Note: For greater durability and ease of use, copy the pieces below onto cardstock or construction paper.

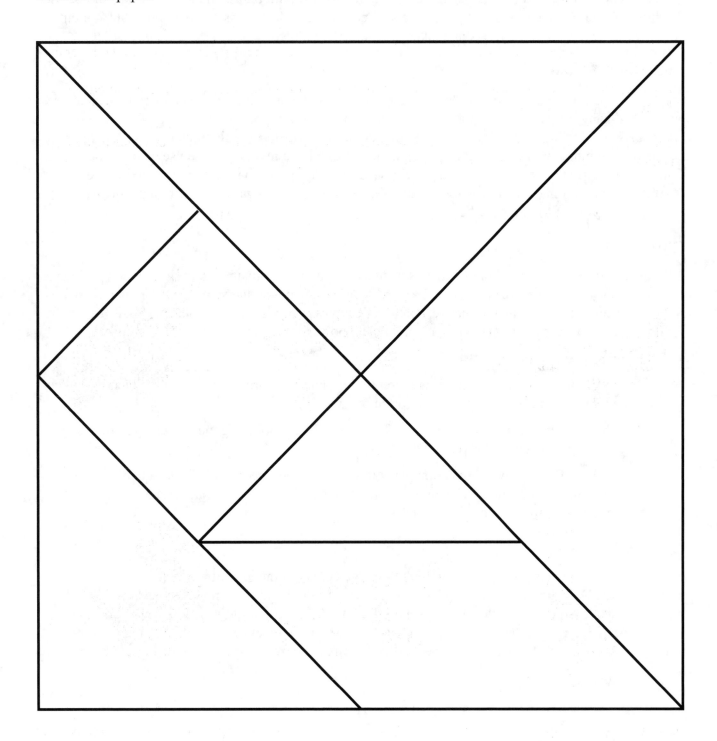

A National Crisis

While athletes around the world are training for their Olympic showdowns in Beijing, the country of China has already begun to battle a fierce opponent that grows stronger by the day: environmental pollution. A thick, gray smog often clouds China's air; and this has severely affected the health of the Chinese people. Respiratory and heart diseases related to air pollution are the leading causes of death in China. Water shortages and pollution are also a constant problem. It is estimated that 90% of city groundwater and 75% of the rivers and lakes in China are polluted.

How the Problem Grew

For decades, China's economy has been built on industry and manufacturing. The main focus had been on making many products in the quickest and least expensive way possible. These products are mainly for *exporting*, which means they are sold to other countries. This economic model (or way of doing business), combined with China's huge population, led to a large increase in the use of fossil fuels. When fossil fuels (such as coal) burn, they release greenhouse gases that damage the environment. A 2007 study found that China was responsible for more greenhouse gases than any other country (passing the United States for the first time).

China's Plan

In June of 2007, over 1,000 Chinese citizens were asked about their country's environmental problems. Most (88%) said that they were concerned about climate change. At that same time, China released its National Action Plan on Climate Change. Much of China's plan focuses on replacing fossil fuels with sources of renewable energy like hydropower, nuclear power, and biofuels.

- **Hydropower** uses water to create energy and electricity. China has the most hydro-electric capacity in the world. The country is currently building the Three Gorges Dam, which will likely be the largest hydro-electric power station in the world.

- China has nine **nuclear power** facilities. The plan calls for doubling the percentage of electricity created by this source by the year 2020.

- China's State Forestry Administration plans to use 13 million hectares (50,000 square miles) of land for **biofuel** production. This process uses plants and other organic materials to create fuel that can be used in cars and other vehicles.

Green Olympics

One of the main concepts of the Beijing 2008 Olympic Games is the idea of a Green Olympics. This means that the host country is working hard to make the Beijing 2008 Olympic Games as positive for the environment as possible. Eleven new venues have been built to hold Olympic competitions, and each has been designed to decrease energy costs and create less pollution. China is taking great pride in its efforts to fight pollution, and it hopes to show the results to the world in August of 2008.

New Ways to Make Energy

For the Beijing 2008 Olympic Games, the host country of China has taken many steps to improve its environment. Many other countries are taking these steps with them. There are no borders when it comes to the environment. What each country does to the air and the water can affect the whole world.

One of the most important ways to help the environment is to find new ways to create the energy people need. We use energy to do everything from driving our cars to cooking our food to keeping ourselves cool in the summertime. For centuries, people have mostly used fossil fuels to do this. But these fuels harm our environment and the people, animals, and plants in it. These fuels are also non-renewable, which means there is a limited supply of them on Earth. We will eventually run out of them. So finding renewable sources of energy is very important to everyone.

The chart below lists several sources of renewable energy that are being used more and more. Use an encyclopedia or the Internet to research each one and complete the chart.

Energy Source	Advantages	Disadvantages
water power		
nuclear power		
solar power		
wind power		
biofuels		

Bird's Nest and Water Cube

The place where an athletic event is held is called a *venue*. Often venues are stadiums, but they can also be open waterways where sailing events are held or bumpy trails where mountain bike races take place. For the Beijing 2008 Olympic Games, there will be a whopping 37 venues needed to hold all of the events. Thirty-one of the venues are in the city of Beijing, and six are located in nearby cities.

Of all these venues, the two that will most likely be the "faces" of the Beijing 2008 Olympic Games are Beijing National Stadium ("The Bird's Nest") and the Beijing National Aquatics Center ("The Water Cube"). Both have been built especially for the Beijing 2008 Olympic Games.

Beijing National Stadium is called "The Bird's Nest" because of its unique design. The materials used to build the structure crisscross each other like twigs in a bird's nest. The Games will begin in this venue with the Opening Ceremonies on August 8, and they will end there too, when the Closing Ceremonies take place on August 24. The Bird's Nest will also host many football (soccer) and track-and-field events. During the Games, the stadium will seat up to 100,000 spectators.

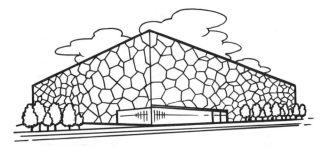

Next door to "The Bird's Nest" will be the Beijing National Aquatics Center. This Olympic venue seats 17,000 people and will host all of the swimming and diving competitions. From the outside, it looks just like a cube made of water. The outside will be covered in a special plastic that will greatly help to reduce energy costs.

Activity: After reading the passage, fill in the circle next to each correct answer below.

1. How many Olympic venues are located in the city of Beijing?
   - (a) 37
   - (b) 31
   - (c) 6

2. In which century were these two venues built?
   - (a) 21st century
   - (b) 20th century
   - (c) 16th century

3. This sporting event will take place in "The Water Cube."
   - (a) sailing
   - (b) judo
   - (c) synchronized swimming

4. This sporting event will **not** take place in "The Bird's Nest."
   - (a) gymnastics
   - (b) 100-meter sprint
   - (c) long jump

5. About how many more people can fit in "The Bird's Nest" than can fit in "The Water Cube"?
   - (a) 83,000
   - (b) 100,000
   - (c) 17,000

The Olympic Slogan

A slogan is a short, memorable phrase that is used to give people an idea about something. When the Beijing Olympic Committee worked together to make a slogan for the Beijing 2008 Olympic Games, they wanted a phrase that represented all that the event would stand for. They thought about the concepts and ideals of the Beijing 2008 Olympic Games. They thought of the concept of the Green Olympics, which promotes the idea of the harmony between people and nature. They thought about the concept of the People's Olympics, which introduces the world to Chinese culture and welcomes new cultures into China. They thought of the concept of the High-tech Olympics, which moves China and the rest of the world forward toward a better life.

To find out the slogan they came up with, you have to solve a puzzle first. The Olympic Slogan for the Beijing 2008 Olympic Games is hidden in the boxes below. Move the gray letters from the bottom rows up to fill in the chart. Be careful, though: the letters in each column might be mixed up! Cross out each letter as you use it. A few letters have been placed for you.

The Puzzle

■	O			■
		R		
■			E	■
				M

The Letters

D	Ø	X̸	A	D
W	O	E	E̸	M̸
	O	N	E	
	R	N	L	

Write the Olympic Slogan here: _____

Do you think this is a good slogan for the Beijing 2008 Olympic Games? Explain your answer.

_____

_____

The Flame of Beijing

The Olympic flame is one of the most important symbols of the Games. It was originally meant as a sign of truce between athletes to put aside the differences of their countries. Each Olympiad, hundreds of people throughout the world participate in the torch relay by carrying the Olympic flame from the site of the Ancient Olympic Games (Olympia, Greece) to the site of the current Olympic Games. The tradition started during the Berlin Olympic Games of 1936.

The Beijing Olympic Torch was designed with the three concepts of the Beijing 2008 Olympic Games in mind. Those concepts are the Green Olympics, the High-tech Olympics, and the People's Olympics.

Here are several facts about the torch's design, as well as the themes and slogans it is meant to represent. Read each one and match it to the concept (Green Olympics, High-tech Olympics, or People's Olympics) that it best expresses. In the appropriate boxes below, write the letters given next to each fact.

A – The torch uses a clean-burning fuel that doesn't produce pollution.

B – The torch contains such traditional Chinese images as paper scrolls and lucky clouds.

C – The torch is designed to stay lighted in such weather conditions as strong wind, rain, snow, and hail.

D – The theme of the torch expresses traditional Chinese beliefs in the balance between man andnature.

E – The flame is designed so that it can be photographed in sunshine and other bright conditions.

F – The torch is built from recyclable materials.

G – The theme of the relay is "Journey of Harmony." This supports the Chinese people's wish of building a society of peace and prosperity.

People's Olympics		
Green Olympics		**High-tech Olympics**

One Flame, Two Journeys

The Olympic flame is passed from hand to hand and from country to country. This relay symbolizes peace, respect, and friendship among all peoples and nations. The torch's long journey is only possible through the cooperation of all who share in its travels.

Here is the itinerary (travel schedule) of the Olympic flame in 2008:

March 25 — The Olympic flame is lighted at Olympia, Greece.

March 31 — The flame arrives in Beijing, and a second torch is lighted. That torch stays in Beijing, while the other begins its relay around the world. From Beijing, the flame travels to each continent (other than Antarctica), making several stops in Europe and Asia. The torch's only stop in North America will be in San Francisco, California.

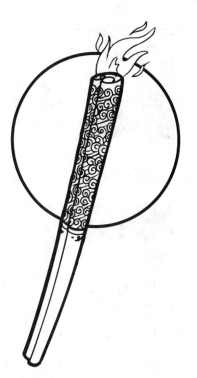

May 4 — The torch returns to China and begins its 113-city tour of the Chinese provinces.

August 6 — The torch arrives back in Beijing.

August 8 — The torch is used to light the Olympic flame at the opening ceremonies of the Beijing 2008 Olympic Games.

What do you think happens with the torch that is left behind in Beijing on March 31? The answer is that torch will attempt to make history. When the weather conditions are at their best, a climber will attempt to take the Olympic flame to the highest peak of Mt. Qomolangma near the southern border of Tibet, China. Mt. Qomolangma is the highest mountain in the world. In the West, Mt. Qomolangma is known as Mt. Everest.

If the torch were staying in your city, state, province, or country, where would you want it to be lighted? What one place—natural or manmade—would best represent your area and the ideals of the Olympic Games?

Name that place here: _____

Explain why you chose this place: _____

_____

_____

_____

Olympic Games Sports

There will be 28 different sports featured in the Beijing 2008 Olympic Games, and some of those sports have several disciplines. (A discipline is a sub-category of the sport that has its own rules.) Below and on pages 37–41 are the descriptions of each Olympic sport.

Aquatics   *Olympic Sport Since 1896*

All of the water sports—including diving, swimming, synchronized swimming, water polo—belong to the category of aquatics.

Olympic Memory: In 1972, an American swimmer named Mark Spitz won seven gold medals, the most in history for a single Olympic Games.

Archery   *Olympic Sport Since 1900*

Archers take hold of their bows and aim their arrows at distant targets. This sport takes strong hands, sharp eyes, and steady nerves.

Olympic Memory: Archery was an Olympic sport from 1900–1920, but then disappeared for over 50 years. In 1972 it came back and has been an Olympic sport ever since.

Athletics (Track and Field)   *Olympic Sport Since 1896*

Some of the world's greatest athletes compete in these track-and-field events. The popular sport of athletics includes most of the running, jumping, and throwing competitions.

Olympic Memory: In 1948, an American named Bob Mathias became the youngest person to win the Olympic decathlon. He was only 17 years old.

Badminton   *Olympic Sport Since 1992*

In this game, players use rackets to slam a shuttlecock (which is made of cork and goose feathers) over a net. The shuttlecock has been clocked at speeds of over 161 miles (260 km) per hour, making badminton the world's fastest racket sport.

Olympic Memory: In both 1996 and 2000, Ge Fei and Gu Jun took home the gold in the doubles competitions. The two Chinese women had been playing together since they were nine years old.

Olympic Games Sports *(cont.)*

Baseball   *Olympic Sport Since 1992*

This sport features nine starters on each team battling for nine innings to see who can score the most runs. Unfortunately, it has been decided that baseball (along with softball) will not be a part of the 2012 Olympic Games in London, England.

Olympic Memory: In 1996, Omar Linares hit three home runs in the final game to help Cuba beat Japan 13–9.

Basketball   *Olympic Sport Since 1936*

Teams of five battle each other on a hardwood court. The men's version of this game has traditionally been dominated by teams from the United States.

Olympic Memory: In the 1936 Games, basketball was played on an outdoor dirt court. It rained on the day of the final, and the two teams could barely dribble the ball in the mud. The U.S. beat Canada in a very low-scoring game (19–8).

Boxing   *Olympic Sport Since 1904*

This brutal test of speed, strength, stamina, and courage was twice banned from Olympic competition (in 1896 and 1912). The sport's Olympic origins go all the way back to the Ancient Olympic Games.

Olympic Memory: When he beat American Jose Torres in 1956, Laszlo Papp from Hungary became the first boxer to win three gold medals.

Canoeing/Kayaking   *Olympic Sport Since 1936*

There are two disciplines in this Olympic sport: flatwater and slalom. Flatwater racing takes place in lanes on calm waters. In slalom racing, the paddlers must make their way through rough waters.

Olympic Memory: German canoeist Birgit Fischer is the only woman to win gold medals more than 20 years apart. She won gold in 1980, 1988, 1992, 1996, 2000, and 2004.

Cycling   *Olympic Sport Since 1896*

There will be four cycling disciplines in 2008: 1. BMX (includes jumps and other obstacles), 2. Road (timed race, long distances), 3. Track (fast speeds around an angled track), 4. Mountain Bike (a hilly course covered with trees, rocks, branches, and streams).

Olympic Memory: In 1896, the road cycling event was held on the same course as the marathon race.

Olympic Games Sports *(cont.)*

Equestrian   *Olympic Sport Since 1900*

This is the only Olympic sport where people compete with animals (though equestrian events are a part of the modern pentathlon). The horse and its rider combine speed, grace, and artistry to complete certain movements, steps, and jumps.

Olympic Memory: In the early part of the 20th century, only members of the military were allowed to compete in the equestrian discipline called *Eventing*.

Fencing   *Olympic Sport Since 1896*

Opponents face off and try to score points on each other with one of three types of weapons. When using a foil, one can score points by striking the opponent's torso. With the epee, one can strike an opponent anywhere on the body. When using a sabre, strikes are restricted to above the waist.

Olympic Memory: In 1920, Italian Nedo Nadi became the only fencer to win the gold medal in each of the three weapons.

Football (Soccer)   *Olympic Sport Since 1900*

Widely considered to be the most popular sport in the world, this game pits two teams of 11 players each against each other. Strategy and stamina are needed to excel in this sport where few goals are scored and much running is required.

Olympic Memory: In 2000, Patrick Mboma and his teammates from the African nation of Cameroon unexpectedly won the gold after beating great teams from Brazil and Spain.

Gymnastics   *Olympic Sport Since 1896*

In the Olympic Games, there are three different disciplines: artistic, rhythmic, and trampoline. In each of these, the athletes combine incredible balance and gracefulness with power and strength to perform a series of skills.

Olympic Memory: Despite having a badly sprained ankle, U.S. gymnast Kerri Strug landed her last vault perfectly to seal the victory for the women's team in 1996.

Handball   *Olympic Sport Since 1936*

In this fast-paced, high-energy game, athletes use their hands to dribble, pass, and catch a small ball. Two teams of seven players each compete to score the most goals.

Olympic Memory: Sweden's handball team won the silver medal in three straight Olympiads (1992, 1996, and 2000).

Olympic Games Sports *(cont.)*

Hockey
Olympic Sport Since 1908

In this ancient game played on grass, athletes use a crooked stick to shoot a small ball into a net. There is evidence that this sport was played as long ago as 2000 BCE in Persia.

Olympic Memory: Teams from India once dominated this sport, as they won 6 straight gold medals from 1928 to 1956.

Judo
Olympic Sport Since 1964

What's in a name? The word *judo* may mean "the gentle way" in Japanese, but this sport comes from an ancient style of hand-to-hand combat.

Olympic Memory: In 1996, a 16-year-old Korean girl named Sun-Hi Kye defeated Ryoko Tamura, a Japanese athlete who had not lost in her last 84 matches.

Modern Pentathlon
Olympic Sport Since 1912

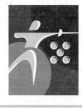

The multi-talented stars of this sport compete in five events. In order, they are shooting, fencing, swimming, show jumping (on horse), and running.

Olympic Memory: In 2000, Stephanie Cook from Great Britain became the first woman to win the gold in this sport.

Rowing
Olympic Sport Since 1896

There are two main types of rowing races: sweep oar (where the rower has one oar) and sculling (where the rower has two oars). Each boat contains one, two, four, or eight rowers, depending on the event.

Olympic Memory: A British rower named Steve Redgrave won gold medals in five straight Olympic Games (1984–2000).

Sailing
Olympic Sport Since 1900

There will be 11 sailing events in 2008. In Olympic sailing, boats of the same class or design are raced against each other.

Olympic Memory: In 1988, a sudden storm knocked two sailors from Singapore into the water and injured them. A Canadian sailor named Lawrence Lemieux saw this and immediately went to their rescue. He lost his chance to win the race but became a hero instead.

Olympic Games Sports *(cont.)*

Shooting

Olympic Sport Since 1896

In the Olympic Games, there are four different types of shooting events: shotgun, rifle, pistol, and running-target events.

Olympic Memory: In 1920, a 72-year-old Swedish shooter named Oscar Swahn became the oldest Olympian. He won a silver medal.

Softball

Olympic Sport Since 1996

Even though the ball used in this women's team sport is larger, it may be even harder to hit than a baseball. The pitchers stand much closer and deliver the ball at speeds of 70 miles (112.5 km) per hour.

Olympic Memory: The U.S. softball team has won gold in every Olympiad so far (1996, 2000, 2004). Will they make it four in a row in 2008?

Table Tennis

Olympic Sport Since 1988

Millions of people play this paddle game (also known as Ping-Pong) for fun, but few can compete in the Olympic Games. When players at this level strike the ball, it can travel at speeds of up to 100 miles (160 km) per hour.

Olympic Memory: In 1992, Yeping Deng and Qiao Hong won gold as partners in the doubles event. A few days later, they faced each other as opponents in the singles competition. Yeping Deng came away with the gold.

Taekwondo

Olympic Sport Since 2000

Taekwondo means "the way of kicking and striking," and it is the traditional martial art of Korea. Athletes use their hands and especially their feet to defeat their opponents.

Olympic Memory: In 2000, Korea's Kyung-Hun Kim became the first heavyweight Olympic champion.

Tennis

Olympic Sport Since 1896

This court game can be played in singles (one on one) or doubles (two on two). In doubles play, the court is wider.

Olympic Memory: Suzanne Lenglen of France lost only one match between 1919 and 1926. During that time, she won two gold medals.

Olympic Games Sports *(cont.)*

Triathlon

A grueling test of stamina and endurance, the triathlon consists of three consecutive events: a 2.4-mile (3.86 km) swim, a 112-mile (180.2 km) bike race, and a full 26.2-mile (42.2 km) marathon run.

Olympic Memory: In 2000, a Canadian triathlete named Simon Whitfield was in 24th place when the running portion of the event began. Slowly he worked his way closer to the leader, and he finally sprinted into the lead with about 200 meters (219 yards) left in the race.

Volleyball
Olympic Sport Since 1964

This Olympic sport is unique in that it can be played on a hardwood court or on a sandy beach. In the court version, each team has six starting players and available substitutes. In beach volleyball, each team is made up of just two people.

Olympic Memory: In 1988, Karch Kiraly and Steve Timmons led the U.S. men's team to its second straight Olympic gold medal.

Weightlifting
Olympic Sport Since 1896

This sport showcases strength in its purest form. Since the beginning of the Olympic Games, the world's strongest men have competed in this sport. In 2000, women's weightlifting became an Olympic event.

Olympic Memory: American Tommy Kono won Olympic medals (two gold, one silver) in three different weight classes from 1952 to 1960.

Wrestling
Olympic Sport Since 1896

This may be the oldest of all competitive sports. For the Olympic Games, wrestling comes in two disciplines: Greco-Roman and freestyle. In Greco-Roman, wrestlers can only use their arms and upper bodies to defeat opponents. Trips, pushes, and other leg moves are allowed in freestyle wrestling.

Olympic Memory: In one of the greatest upsets in Olympic history, American Rulon Gardner defeated a great Russian wrestler named Aleksandr Karelin. Before the match, Karelin had not lost in 13 years.

The Olympic Program

The 17 days of the Beijing 2008 Olympic Games will be a busy time! With the many different sports played in 37 venues, the Olympic action will be thrilling and constant. Here is the schedule. Check it to see when your favorite sports will be played. Then take the Olympic Program Challenge on page 43.

August 2008	8	9	10	11	12	13	14	15	16	17	18	19	20	21	22	23	24
Day	F	S	S	M	T	W	T	F	S	S	M	T	W	T	F	S	S
Opening Ceremonies	●																
Aquatics		●	●	●	●	●	●	●	●	●	●	●	●	●	●	●	●
Archery		●	●	●	●	●	●	●									
Athletics								●	●	●	●	●	●	●	●	●	●
Badminton		●	●	●	●	●	●	●	●	●							
Baseball						●	●	●	●	●	●	●	●	●	●		
Basketball		●	●	●	●	●	●	●	●	●	●	●	●	●	●	●	●
Boxing		●	●	●	●	●	●	●	●	●	●	●			●	●	●
Canoe/Kayak				●	●		●				●	●	●	●	●	●	
Cycling		●	●			●		●	●	●		●					
Equestrian		●	●	●	●	●	●	●	●	●	●	●	●	●			
Fencing		●	●	●	●	●	●	●	●	●							
Football (Soccer)		●	●		●	●		●	●		●	●		●	●	●	
Gymnastics		●	●		●	●		●	●	●	●	●	●	●	●	●	●
Handball		●	●	●	●	●	●	●	●	●	●	●	●	●	●	●	●
Hockey			●	●	●	●	●	●	●	●	●	●	●	●	●		
Judo		●	●	●	●	●	●	●									
Modern Pentathlon														●	●		
Rowing		●	●	●	●	●	●	●	●	●							
Sailing		●	●	●	●	●	●	●	●	●	●	●	●	●	●		
Shooting		●	●	●	●	●	●	●	●	●							
Softball					●	●	●	●	●	●	●	●	●	●			
Table Tennis						●	●	●	●	●	●	●	●	●	●	●	
Taekwondo													●	●	●	●	
Tennis			●	●	●	●	●	●	●	●							
Triathlon											●	●					
Volleyball		●	●	●	●	●	●	●	●	●	●	●	●	●	●	●	●
Weightlifting		●	●	●	●	●		●	●	●	●	●					
Wrestling					●	●	●		●	●		●	●	●			
Closing Ceremonies																	●

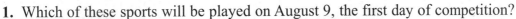

The Olympic Program Challenge

Use "The Olympic Program" on page 42 to answer the following questions. Fill in the circle next to the correct answer.

1. Which of these sports will be played on August 9, the first day of competition?

   ⓐ    ⓑ    ⓒ

2. Which of these sports is the last to begin competition?

   ⓐ   ⓑ   ⓒ

3. Which of these sports is played on the least amount of days?

   ⓐ    ⓑ   ⓒ

4. Which of these sports will not be played on Sunday, August 17?

   ⓐ    ⓑ   ⓒ

5. Which of these sports is the first to finish competition?

   ⓐ    ⓑ    ⓒ

6. Which of these sports has a total of 16 days of competition?

   ⓐ    ⓑ   ⓒ

7. Name three sports that do not have a competition on a Monday.

   _____   _____   _____

Sports Categories

In total, there will be 28 sports featured in the Beijing 2008 Olympic Games. Some of them have things in common with other sports. Some are completely unique. Write down every sport that fits into these categories.

· AQUATICS · ARCHERY · ATHLETICS · BADMINTON · BASEBALL · BASKETBALL · BOXING

WRESTLING · WEIGHTLIFTING · VOLLEYBALL · TRIATHLON · TENNIS · TAEKWONDO · TABLE TENNIS ·

CANOEING/KAYAKING · CYCLING · EQUESTRIAN · FENCING · FOOTBALL · GYMNASTICS · HANDBALL

Water Sports

Sports Played on a Court

Sports That Use a Ball

Sports That Use a Horse

Hand-to-Hand Combat Sports

Sports That Use a Weapon

·HOCKEY · MODERN PENTATHLON · ROWING · SAILING · SHOOTING · SOFTBALL

You Make the Choice

In 1896, there were only nine sports scheduled to be a part of the first Modern Olympic Games. The number has since grown to include 28 sports. How did that happen? The International Olympic Committee (IOC) meets each year to make many decisions about the Olympic Games. They choose the host cities, and they also decide which sports should be included on the program. Many sports have been added in recent years, and some have even been subtracted. In 2008, for instance, BMX cycling will make its Olympic debut. Baseball and softball, however, will be discontinued after the Beijing 2008 Olympic Games.

Look at pages 36–41 for a list of the 28 sports on the 2008 program. What sports are missing? Are there any that you think should be a part of the Olympic Games? Now is your chance to state your opinion. Fill out the form below with a sport that is not currently a part of the Olympic Games. You can pick your favorite sport, or you can create a whole new sport of your own.

Name of the Sport

_____

Uniform	Equipment
Draw here.	Draw here.
Describe here.	Describe here.
_____	_____
_____	_____
_____	_____

How the Sport Is Played

_____

_____

_____

_____

Track and Field Puzzle

One of the most popular sports in the Olympic Games is athletics, or track and field as it is often called. There are many different events that are a part of athletics. Most foot races are considered track events. Most events that involve jumping or throwing things are field events. There are also events like the decathlon, which combine the two. Athletes who participate in the decathlon have to complete 10 different skills.

Fill out the crossword puzzle below with the names of track events (the **Across** words) and field events (the **Down** words). Use the clues to help you.

Track (Across)

4. Athletes run a course that includes several jumps, some over water-filled ditches.
6. This object is handed from one runner to the next in a relay race.
7. Athletes run a course that includes 10 jumps over obstacles that will fall if hit.
8. This metric unit of measurement is used for all short- and medium-distance Olympic races.

Field (Down)

1. Athletes throw a long spear as far as they can.
2. Athletes run, then hop once and skip once, before jumping on their third bounce.
3. Athletes use a long pole to push themselves over a very high bar.
4. Athletes use a pushing motion to throw a heavy metal ball.
5. Athletes spin as they throw a plate-shaped object for distance.

Challenge: Can you name the 10 different events that make up the decathlon?

_____   _____

_____   _____   _____

_____   _____   _____

_____   _____

Gymnastics Roll Call

To many, the athletes who compete in the discipline of artistic gymnastics seem to do the impossible. They fly and twist through the air; they twirl their entire bodies around a bar; they jump and land on the narrowest of surfaces.

Part I: Read the descriptions below. Each names an incredible feat that a gymnast routinely performs. Can you match each to the Olympic event it describes? Use the events listed in the box to help you.

> **Gymnastics Events**
>
> A. balance beam   C. vault   E. pommel horse
>
> B. floor exercise   D. parallel bars

_____ 1. The gymnast sprints down a runway, jumps onto a springboard, and then pushes off on a piece of equipment as he or she is going forward. The gymnast twirls and spins before landing.

_____ 2. The gymnast holds himself up on two bars that are the same height and about a shoulder's width apart. He performs swings and jumps before dismounting.

_____ 3. The gymnast performs an artistic show on a large square of carpet. He or she runs, tumbles, flips, and leaps and must touch each corner of the square at least once.

_____ 4. The gymnast performs a routine that includes leaps, turns, and dance moves—all while standing on a 4-inch-wide (10 cm) piece of equipment that is over 4 feet (120 cm) off the ground.

_____ 5. The gymnast must perform continuous circular movements while holding onto a piece of equipment that he can only touch with his hands. Great balance is required.

Part II: The discipline of artistic gymnastics includes many events. A few are competed in by both men and women, but most are not. Conduct an online search to find out who competes in the different events. In the left section, write the events that are only for men. In the right section, write those that only women compete in. In the middle section, name the events that both men and women perform in.

	Both	
Men's Events		**Women's Events**

Olympic Ideals

One of the greatest goals of the Olympic Games is to bring out the best in people—not just as athletes, but also as neighbors. Two ideals that best illustrate this goal are the Olympic Truce and the Olympic Creed.

The Olympic Truce

The Olympic Games is an event that promotes peace and the breaking down of borders between countries and cultures. But the world is not always a peaceful place. Often, countries are at war with each other. That is why the Olympic Truce is so important. A truce is an agreement to stop fighting.

The Truce began all the way back in the time of the Ancient Olympic Games. It was called *Ekekeiria* back then, and it allowed Greek athletes and citizens to travel to the Games without fear of being attacked. The truce was announced just before the first day of the Games, and it lasted until the athletes had returned home safely. Today, the General Assembly of the United Nations announces the truce one year before the Games begin and asks that all nations recognize its importance.

Do you think the Olympic Truce is less important or more important now than it was back in the time of the Ancient Greeks? Explain your answer.

The Olympic Creed

The Olympic Creed is a standard that all athletes who compete in the Olympic Games try to live up to. This is what is says:

> *"The most important thing in the Olympic Games is not to win, but to take part,*
> *just as the most important thing in life is not the triumph but the struggle.*
> *The essential thing is not to have conquered but to have fought well."*

List three ways that you think an athlete can honor the Olympic Creed.

1. _____

   _____

2. _____

   _____

3. _____

   _____

List one way that you think an athlete could dishonor the Olympic Creed.

_____

_____

An Unlikely Friendship

The 1936 Olympic Games were held in Berlin, Germany, during a very tense time in world history. 1936 was three years *after* Adolf Hitler and the Nazi Party had become the ruling party in Germany and three years *before* their attacks on other peoples, races, and countries began World War II. One of the Nazi Party's main beliefs was that white people who came from a specific northern European race were superior to (better than) people from other races.

Into this climate of racial tension came athletes from 49 nations. One of those athletes was a great African-American track-and-field star named Jesse Owens.

Jesse proved he was a great athlete in his first competition of the 1936 Games when he won the gold medal in the 100-meter sprint. The next day was August 4, 1936, and it was on this day that a white German athlete named Carl "Lutz" Long showed the true meaning of sportsmanship.

On that day, the long jump event was held. In the first round, Long set an Olympic record with his jump. Owens, however, fouled on his first two jumps. Each time, he accidentally stepped over the line as he began his jump. If he fouled on his third and final try, he would not be allowed to jump again. After his second jump, Owens was so upset that he sat down on some nearby grass to think. That's when Long came over and gave Owens some advice. He told him to try to take off from further back. He knew that Owens could jump far enough if he just made sure not to foul. With Long's encouragement, Owens ran and jumped from well behind the line. His jump was good this time, and he went on to the next round. In the end, Owens went on to earn the gold medal in the long jump. One of his jumps even broke the Olympic record that Long had set earlier in the day. After Owens's great jump, Long was the first one to come over and congratulate him. The two new friends even walked off the field together as they talked.

Owens went on to win a total of four gold medals at the 1936 Olympic Games. Later, he said of Long, "It took a lot of courage for him to befriend me in front of Hitler. You can melt down all the medals and cups I have, and they wouldn't [come close to equaling the] friendship I felt for Lutz Long at that moment."

Activity: Read "Olympic Ideals" on page 48. In your own words, tell how Lutz Long lived up to the spirit of sportsmanship described in both the Olympic Truce and the Olympic Creed. Use a separate piece of paper.

Sun + Moon = All-Star

The doctors in a Shanghai hospital knew that the baby born on September 12, 1980, was special. The newborn weighed 11 pounds (5 kg), twice the size of the average Chinese baby. This was somewhat to be expected considering the size of the baby's parents: the mother was 6'2" (1.88 m) and the father was 6'8" (2.08 m). The parents named the baby Ming, after a Chinese character that unifies (brings together) the sun and the moon.

Yao Ming started off bigger than most, and he just kept growing. He was 5'5" (1.65 m) by age 10; and by the time he turned 13 years old, he stood 6'6" (2 m) tall. Yao began playing basketball when he was nine, and he quickly caught the eyes of the Chinese government and of corporate sponsors and shoe companies. Yao spent his teens practicing basketball over 10 hours a day. He began to dominate his competition in China; and by the time Yao was 18, coaches from the National Basketball Association (NBA) were following his every move.

In 2002, Yao Ming decided to enter the NBA amateur draft. The Houston Rockets had the first pick of that draft, and they knew that Yao was the man they wanted on their team. By picking the 7'6" center from China, the Rockets made Yao the first player without any American basketball experience to be selected first overall in an NBA draft.

A lot of people wondered if Yao was just a tall guy. Could he really play basketball? Would he be able to match up against great NBA players like Shaquille O'Neal? One thing was for sure: whatever Yao did, half of the world—from China in the East to California in the West—would be watching.

During his rookie (first) year in the NBA, Yao proved that he belonged. He played in all of the Rockets' games and came in second in the voting for the NBA Rookie of the Year Award. He even beat out fellow center O'Neal when he was voted the starting player at his position for the Western Conference All-Star team.

Yao followed up the success of his rookie year by leading his team to the playoffs in his second year. Again, he played every game for his team, and again, he was voted the starter on the All-Star team.

The Athens 2004 Olympic Games took place in the summer between Yao's second and third NBA seasons. Yao began those Olympic Games by living a "dream come true": he was chosen to carry the Chinese flag during the opening ceremonies. During the competition, Yao led China into the quarterfinal round where they eventually lost. His individual performance, however, earned him a selection on the All-Olympics team.

Yao Ming

Sun + Moon = All-Star (cont.)

By his third NBA season, Yao Ming's popularity around the globe was undeniable. In the voting for the 2005 All-Star Game, he received 2,558,278 fan votes, shattering the record previously held by the great Michael Jordan.

During the 2005–2006 and 2006–2007 seasons, Yao's game got even better, but his luck took a turn for the worse. He suffered several foot and leg injuries during those seasons and missed many games for the first time in his career. Despite these setbacks, Yao's numbers (points per game, rebounds per game, etc.) increased each year. So far, Yao Ming has proven that he is more than just a tall guy on the basketball court.

1. What city's NBA team drafted Yao Ming in 2002?

    (a) Los Angeles   (b) Houston   (c) Dallas

2. Which of these flags did Yao Ming carry during the opening ceremonies of the 2004 Olympic Games?

    (a)   (b)   (c)

3. Michael Jordan once held the record of most fan votes for an All-Star Game with 2,451,136. How many more votes did Yao Ming receive when he broke the record?

    (a) 2,558,278   (b) 97,412   (c) 107,142

What Do You Think?

Part I: Yao Ming came to America in 2002, and by 2005 he had already become one of the most popular players in the U.S. Can you think of other people (athletes, celebrities, etc.) who have found success in a country other than the one in which they grew up? List three, and give a reason why you think they were successful.

_____

_____

_____

_____

Part II: If you could have success in a foreign country like Yao Ming has had in the United States, which country would you choose? Give at least three reasons for your answer.

_____

_____

_____

_____

Legendary Olympians

The history of the Olympic Games is filled with incredible athletes who performed amazing feats when the spotlight shone the brightest on them.

Directions: Learn about an Olympic legend. Choose one from the list below (or pick one of your own) and make an Athlete Trading Card (see page 53) for him or her. Use an encyclopedia or the Internet to do your research.

Aquatics
Amanda Beard
Matt Biondi
Janet Evans
Dawn Fraser
Michael Gross
Greg Louganis
Patricia McCormick
Michael Phelps
Mark Spitz
Johnny Weissmuller

Archery
Soo-Nyung Kim

Athletics
Abebe Bikila
Sebastian Coe
Mildred "Babe" Didrikson
Ray Ewry
Dick Fosbury
Michael Johnson
Jackie Joyner-Kersee
Carl Lewis
Bob Mathias
Edwin Moses
Al Oerter
Jesse Owens
Wilma Rudolph
Jim Thorpe

Badminton
Gu Jun
Ge Fei

Baseball
Orestes Kindelan
Omar Linares

Basketball
Michael Jordan
Earvin "Magic" Johnson

Boxing
Muhammad Ali
Laszlo Papp

Canoeing/Kayaking
Birgit Fischer

Cycling
Paola Pezzo

Equestrian
Reiner Klimke

Fencing
Giovanna Trillini

Football (Soccer)
Mia Hamm

Gymnastics
Nadia Comaneci
Bart Conner
Olga Korbut
Vitaly Scherbo
Kerri Strug

Handball
Magnus Wislander

Hockey
Rechelle Hawkes

Judo
David Douillet

Modern Pentathlon
Lars Hall

Rowing
Steve Redgrave

Sailing
Valentyn Mankin

Shooting
Karoly Takacs

Softball
Lisa Fernandez

Table Tennis
Yaping Deng

Taekwondo
Kyong-Hun Kim

Tennis
Steffi Graf

Triathlon
Simon Whitfield

Volleyball
Charles "Karch" Kiraly
Regla Torres

Weightlifting
Naim Suleymanoglu

Wrestling
Rulon Gardner
Aleksandr Karelin

Athlete Trading Cards

Choose an athlete from the list of Legendary Olympians on page 52. Draw his or her picture (or use one from the Internet or from a magazine or newspaper). Include important details about your athlete in the "Achievements" section. Cut out the shape, fold it in half, and glue the front to the back. Now you've got a pocket-sized history of a great Olympic athlete!

Athlete: _____

Sport: _____

Born: _____

Country: _____

Athletic Achievements

Olympic Medals Earned

Gold

Silver

Bronze

The Paralympic Games

In 2008 the city of Beijing will not only be hosting the Olympic Games; it will also be hosting the Paralympic Games. Since 1960, athletes with disabilities have competed in the Paralympic Games. The word *paralympic* is a combination of the Greek suffix *para*, which means "alongside" or "beside" and the word *Olympics*. The athletes who qualify for the Paralympic Games have such disabilities as the following:

- blindness or visual impairment

- cerebral palsy

- amputation (having a limb partially or completely removed)

- dwarfism

- paraplegia (having legs that are partially or completely paralyzed)

- quadriplegia (having arms and legs that are partially or completely paralyzed)

While the Paralympic Games weren't officially held until 1960, the beginnings of this event can be traced back to 1948. Back then, an English doctor named Ludwig Guttman felt that competition would be helpful in rehabilitating the many soldiers who were severely injured on the battlegrounds of World War II. He helped organize physical competitions between patients.

From those beginnings, the Paralympic Games has grown into a huge international event with thousands of athletes competing in several sports. In 2008, Paralympic athletes will compete in 20 different sports, including athletics, football/soccer, powerlifting, swimming, and wheelchair basketball.

Go to *http://en.beijing2008.cn/paralympic/competition/index.shtml* to learn more about these unique sports and the athletes who excel at them. Choose one of the following activities:

- Write a report or prepare a presentation about one of the Paralympic sports. Give details about the equipment needed to play the sport. Explain how disabled athletes are able to perform the tasks each sport demands of them.

- Pick a sport and create a compare-and-contrast chart. On the left side, list all of the things that Olympic athletes and Paralympic athletes have in common. On the right side, list all of the special challenges that Paralympic athletes face as they compete in this sport.

- Do research on a specific Paralympic athlete. Write or speak about the obstacles this athlete has faced on his or her way to becoming a Paralympic athlete.

The Beijing 2008 Paralympic Games will be played from September 6 to September 17.

Running Without Legs

From the country of South Africa there comes an athlete so remarkable that he has become the subject of much debate. His name is Oscar Pistorius, and he has no legs. What he does have, though, is world-class running speed. He has been clocked at these unbelievable times: 10.91 seconds in the 100 meters, 21.58 seconds in the 200 meters, and 46.56 seconds in the 400 meters. While those times are each a few seconds shy of Olympic and world records, they are the best times ever run by a disabled athlete. They put him on the cusp of qualifying for not only the Paralympic Games, but also the Olympic Games.

When Oscar was born in November of 1986, he had no fibula bones. Those are the slender bones in a person's lower legs. Before Oscar reached the age of one, this condition forced doctors to amputate (cut off) both of his legs below the knees. Since he never knew how to walk with his legs, he was able to learn how to walk and balance himself very naturally with the prosthetics (artificial limbs) he was given by the doctors. He grew up playing such sports as rugby and water polo. Amazingly, he didn't begin to train as a runner until 2004. After less than a year of training, he competed in the 2004 Summer Paralympics in Athens, where he won the gold and broke the world record in the 200-meter event. He is considered the favorite to win the gold in several events at the Beijing 2008 Paralympic Games if he chooses to compete in them.

When Oscar runs, he wears carbon-fiber prosthetics that are shaped like curved blades. This is where the debate begins. Do Oscar's carbon legs give him any advantage that able-bodied runners do not have? There is a rule that bans the use of any technical device that gives an athlete an advantage over other athletes who are not using the device. The International Association of Athletics Federation originally decided that Oscar could not compete in the Beijing 2008 Olympic Games because of his carbon legs. They then withdrew this ban and are in the process of testing Oscar's legs to see if they give him an advantage.

Activity: Divide the classroom into two groups and have a classroom debate. One side will take the position that Oscar should be able to compete against Olympic athletes, and the other side will take the position that his carbon legs give him an unfair advantage. Each side should do research to support their position. Type Oscar's name into a search engine or visit an online encyclopedia for more information about this subject.

Oscar Pistorius

Competing With Gravity

The hammer throw is a track-and-field event that has been a part of the Olympic Games since 1900. The hammer is a metal ball attached to a chain with a handle. The one that the men throw weighs 16 lbs. (7.257 kg), while the women's weighs 8.82 lbs. (4 kg). Competitors start at the back of a circle; they spin their bodies three to four times as they move forward in the circle. The hammer turns with them, and its speed increases as it does so. The thrower then releases the hammer when he or she reaches the front of the circle. The winner is the athlete whose hammer flies the farthest. It sounds simple, but when a thrower steps into that circle to make a throw, it's not really the other competitors that he or she has to fight—it's gravity.

Gravity is basically the curving (bending) of space by an object. But it takes a big, dense object like Earth to curve space enough so that other objects—like books and people and hammers—seem to be pulled towards it. Seem to be pulled, because what's really happening is that objects fall in the direction that space curves. It's almost as if space flows in one direction—towards something like Earth. So, when the hammer is just sitting on the ground, what's really happening is that the ground is stopping the hammer from following the curvature of space. That's why it takes energy to lift things: because pulling an object away from Earth is moving it in the opposite direction of space's "flow."

The thrower uses his or her energy to fight against gravity, spinning around to make the hammer go as fast as possible and then letting it go. That energy is used up as the hammer flies against the force of gravity (the "flow" of space), until the energy keeping the hammer away from the Earth is completely used up. At that point, the hammer starts falling in the direction space curves. Only the ground stops it from falling any farther.

Hammer Throw World Records		
	In Meters	In Yards
Men's	86.74 m	94.86 yd.
Women's	77.80 m	85.08 yd.

What do you think would happen if the hammer-throw competition took place on the moon instead of Earth? Here are some things to think about before answering that question:

- The moon is smaller—about 1/4 the size of Earth.

- The moon has less volume—about 1/50 the volume of Earth.

- The moon has less gravitational pull on its surface—about 1/6 that of Earth.

Activity: On a separate sheet of paper, write a newspaper article or Internet blog about a hammer-throw competition held on the moon. Imagine you are either a reporter covering the event or an athlete participating in it. Have fun and be creative, while trying to be as accurate as possible. Give details like the names of competitors, distances thrown, descriptions of the setting, etc. How far will the hammer fly this time?

The Science of Swimming

The human body is 70% water. With air in your lungs, your body is actually less dense than the water around it—which means that your body basically wants to float! All you need to do is keep your body in a horizontal position as you propel (move) yourself slightly forward using your hands and legs. In other words, you just swim.

But if you try to do it fast or for a very long time, swimming is hard work! It can be difficult to keep your body moving. If it's so easy to float, why is it so hard to keep moving? The answer is all about something called *drag*.

Drag occurs when a solid object (likwe a person) moves through a gas (like air) or a liquid (like water). When an airplane flies, the air—which is just little particles—exerts drag on the plane's body. That means that the plane has to move every one of those particles to the side, and that slows the plane down. Molecules are so light that they float and are much too tiny to see, but a plane is running into billions and billions of them every second—and that adds up! The faster a plane moves, the more it runs into at every moment, and so the more drag it encounters. The more drag it encounters, the more energy it has to use to keep moving. The people who design planes try to make them so that there will be as little drag as possible. The less drag there is, the easier it is for the plane to move. The designers minimize (make as small as possible) drag by the type of skin (covering) they choose and by the shape of the plane. They want a skin that will be as smooth as possible so that the air molecules can move across it more easily; and they want a shape that puts as little of the plane as possible in contact with the air. That's why all planes fly horizontally and why the fastest planes are usually shaped like thin cylinders.

In the pool, drag happens in exactly the same way. Water is just billions and billions of water molecules (H_2O). The fewer molecules a swimmer runs into and the easier those molecules can move across his or her body, the easier it is for the swimmer to move forward. This is why Olympic swimmers all wear bathing caps: because that makes for a smoother surface than a bare head—especially a head with hair. All the Olympic swimmers even shave their body hair or wear smooth suits that cover the entire body: the less hair, the less there is for molecules to run into. Of course, minimizing drag isn't the only thing that allows a swimmer to go fast. But if two equally talented swimmers race against each other, the one who encounters less drag will win every time.

Activity: Try this experiment to see for yourself the results of drag:

- Get a hold of two identical, motorized toy boats, torpedoes, etc.

- Spread some glue all over one of them, then roll it dirt, grass shavings, etc. (nothing heavy, just something that will make the surface less smooth). Let the glue dry.

- Make sure both are set so that they'll go in a straight line and that their motors are set to run at the same speed, place them both in the water with the motors on, then let them go at the same time. Watch the one with less drag move into the lead!

Five-Day Forecast

You're packing for your trip to Beijing and you decide you had better know what the weather will be like. Wait, what's this? The local paper says that the weather will be 30°! That's cold! Doesn't water freeze at 32°? You thought you were going to see running and swimming and field hockey, not skating and skiing and ice hockey. What's going on?

Water does freeze at 32°, but only if you are using the Fahrenheit (F) scale. That's the way of measuring temperature that is used primarily in the United States. But many other countries, including China, use the Celsius (C) scale. On that scale, water freezes at 0° and boils at 100°.

You look more closely at your paper and see that the temperature will be 30°C. Now you are completely confused about what the weather will be. Luckily for you, there is a way to convert Celsius temperatures to Fahrenheit. Here is the formula:

> **To Convert Celsius Temperatures to Fahrenheit**
>
> **1.** Multiply the Celsius temperature by 9.
>
> **2.** Then divide by 5.
>
> **3.** Then add 32 to the result.
>
> *Example:* To convert 30°C to Fahrenheit, 30 x 9 = 270
>
> 270 ÷ 5 = 54; 54 + 32 = 86. Therefore, 30°C = 86°F.

Now look at the five-day forecast below. You've been given the temperature in Celsius. Use a piece of scratch paper to calculate each temperature in Fahrenheit and write your answers on the line. Round your answers up or down to the nearest degree.

Monday	Tuesday	Wednesday	Thursday	Friday
35°C	38°C	31°C	25°C	26°C
_____ °F	_____ °F	_____ °F	_____ °F	_____ °F
Sunny	Sunny	Windy	Cloudy	Partly Cloudy

The Metric System

Just as with measuring temperature, the United States uses a different system of measuring distance, length, and weight than most of the rest of the world. The United States uses the U.S. Customary System, while countries such as China use the metric system. For all Olympic Games, even those hosted by U.S. cities, the metric system is used.

Directions: Answer the measurement questions below. All you need is the Metric Conversion Chart and some scratch paper or a calculator. Round your answers to the nearest whole number.

Metric Conversion Chart

Distance, Height, and Length   *Weight*

1 centimeter = .4 inches or .03 feet   1 gram = .04 ounces

1 meter = 39.4 inches or 3.3 feet   1 kilogram = 2.2 pounds
      or 1.1 yards

1 kilometer = .6 miles

---

1. Olympic divers dive from a platform that is 10 meters above the water.

    10 meters = _____ feet

2. The winner of the men's 100-meter race is often called "World's Fastest Man."

    100 meters = _____ yards

3. In road cycling, women race on a course that is over 120 kilometers long.

    120 kilometers = _____ miles

4. In wrestling, the lightest weight class for men is 55 kilograms.

    55 kilograms = _____ pounds

5. Fencing matches take place on a 14-meter by 1.5-meter playing area.

    14 meters by 1.5 meters = _____ feet by _____ feet

Challenge: The rectangular playing area in fencing is called a *piste*. Using your answers to question #5, what is the perimeter of the piste in a fencing match? What is the area? Give your answers in feet.

Perimeter: _____

Area: _____

Adding Oomph

The Olympic Games are filled with action and drama. Any writing that describes the intensity of an Olympic event needs to be intense, too. Use specific nouns and vivid verbs. Add adjectives and adverbs to spice up your descriptions. And use literary devices such as similes and onomatopoeia to give your story some extra oomph.

Remember . . .

A **simile** is a type of comparison that uses the words *like* or *as*.
Example: Uncle Jake is <u>as skinny as a stalk of celery</u>.

Onomatopoeia is a word formed from the sound associated with what is named.
Example: The rain <u>pinged</u> loudly on the shack's metal roof.

Directions: Fill in the story below with words that match the intensity of a sprint for Olympic gold. The word(s) under each line tell you which part of speech or literary device to use.

The runner _____ his muscles as he awaits the sound of the gun to start the race.
_____*verb*_____

He looks to his left at the other runners. In the _____ sun, he can see sweat dripping
_____*adjective*_____

_____ down the arm of the _____ next to him. He squints his eyes
___*adverb*___ _____*noun*_____

and _____ at the lane in front of him. The countdown begins. The crowd grows
_____*verb*_____

_____, and the noise in the _____ becomes deafening. Then
_____*adjective*_____ _____*noun*_____

" _____ !"—the gun goes off and the race begins. He explodes out of the
_____*onomatopoeia*_____

blocks _____ . The _____
_____*simile*_____ _____*noun*_____

he has been training for all his life has finally come.

Now that you have chosen just the right words and phrases, you will have your readers hooked. They'll want to know how the story ends! Finish it on the lines below.

_____

_____

_____

_____

_____

Create an Olympic Mascot

For each Olympiad, the host country creates mascots that give a fun face to the Games. For 2008, Beijing has created five mascots. Each one is a color of one of the Olympic rings, a symbol that represents all of the nations of the world joining together. As a whole, these five playful mascots are called *fuwa*. They represent the children of China and also the country's most popular animals. They are . . .

- Beibei, the blue fish
- Jingjing, the black panda
- Huanhuan, the red Olympic flame
- Yingying, the yellow Tibetan antelope
- Nini, the green swallow

When you put their names together—Bei Jing Huan Ying Ni—
they say, "Welcome to Beijing" in Chinese.

Imagine that the Olympic Games are coming to your part of the world. You have been chosen to create a mascot that shows the spirit and enthusiasm of the place where you live and also of the Olympic Games. Use the space below to draw your mascot. Don't forget to give your mascot a name.

_____

Mascot's Name

Which One Doesn't Belong?

Directions: Circle the one in each group of four that does not belong.

1. **North-American Olympic host cities**

   Barcelona   St. Louis   Montreal   Atlanta

2. **Sports that were a part of the first Modern Olympic Games in 1896**

   fencing   gymnastics   boxing   wrestling

3. **21st century Olympic host cities**

   Athens   London   Paris   Beijing

4. **Types of tea**

   white   red   green   yellow

5. **Sports to be played in the Beijing 2008 Olympic Games**

   taekwondo   golf   tennis   volleyball

6. **U.S. states where Olympic Games have been held**

   California   Texas   Missouri   Georgia

7. **Years that the Olympic Games took place**

   1908   1936   1944   1972

8. **Treasures of the study of calligraphy in China**

   ink stone   brush   knife   paper

9. **European Olympic host cities**

   Berlin   Amsterdam   Paris   Melbourne

10. **Disciplines of the sport of aquatics**

   diving   water polo   sailing   synchronized swimming

Answer Key

Olympic Vocabulary (page 5)

1. venue
2. CE
3. disciplines
4. modern
5. truce
6. C
7. D
8. A
9. B
10. E

The Ancient Olympic Games (page 6)

Ancient Olympic Games: A, E, F, H, I, K, N

2008 Beijing Olympic Games: B, C, D, G, J, L, M

The Modern Games Challenge (page 9)

Part I: 4, 1, 5, 2, 3

Part II

1. a
2. c
3. a
4. b
5. c
6. c
7. a

The Host Cities Challenge (page 11)

1. Munich, Germany

2. Athens, Paris, London, Los Angeles

3.

Host Countries Graph

	1	2	3	4	5
Australia	▨				
Canada	▨				
China	▨				
France	▨	▨			
Germany	▨	▨			
Greece	▨				
Italy	▨				
Mexico	▨				
United States	▨	▨	▨	▨	
U.S.S.R.	▨				

4. 6; St. Louis, Los Angeles (twice), Mexico City, Montreal, Atlanta

5. 12; 1936–1948; because of World War II

Dynasty Match (page 17)

1122 BCE–256 BCE: Zhou Dynasty

206 BCE–220 CE: Han Dynasty

618 CE–907 CE: Tang Dynasty

1368 CE–1644 CE: Ming Dynasty

1644 CE–1911 CE: Qing Dynasty

1. Ming Dynasty
2. Tang Dynasty
3. Zhou Dynasty
4. Qing Dynasty
5. Han Dynasty
6. Ming Dynasty
7. Tang Dynasty
8. Qing Dynasty
9. Han Dynasty
10. Tang Dynasty

Making Silk (page 21)

Step 1: eggs

Step 2: caterpillars

Step 3: eating

Step 4: cocoons

Step 5: liquid

Step 6: mile

Step 7: moths, destroying

Bonus: sericulture

Scrambled Inventions (page 26)

1. silk
2. chopsticks
3. kite
4. paper
5. fireworks
6. compass
7. printing
8. gunpowder
9. seismograph
10. abacus

Chinese Math Puzzles (page 27)

Magic Square

4	9	2
3	5	7
8	1	6

Yang Hui's Triangle

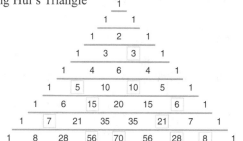

Bird's Nest and Water Cube (page 32)

1. b
2. a
3. c
4. a
5. a

The Olympic Slogan (page 33)

Slogan: "One World, One Dream"

Answer Key (cont.)

The Flame of Beijing (page 34)

Answers may vary. Accept reasonable responses.

Green Olympics: A, F

People's Olympics: B, D, G

High-tech Olympics: C, E

The Olympic Program Challenge (page 43)

1. b
2. a
3. c
4. c
5. b
6. c
7. modern pentathlon, taekwondo, and wrestling

Sports Categories (page 44)

Answer may vary. Accept reasonable and/or creative responses. For example, a student might write "gymnastics" under the category of "Sports That Use a Horse" (pommel horse).

Water Sports: aquatics, canoeing/kayaking, modern pentathlon, rowing, sailing, triathlon

Court Sports: badminton, basketball, handball, tennis, volleyball

Ball Sports: baseball, basketball, football, handball, hockey, softball, table tennis, tennis, volleyball

Horse Sports: equestrian, modern pentathlon

Hand-to-Hand Sports: boxing, judo, taekwondo, wrestling

Weapon Sports: archery, fencing, modern pentathlon, shooting

Track and Field (page 46)

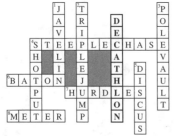

Challenge: The 10 events of the decathlon are the 100-meter sprint, the long jump, the shot put, the high jump, the 400-meter race, the 110-meter hurdles, the discus throw, the pole vault, the javelin throw, and the 1500-meter race.

Gymnastics Roll Call (page 47)

1. C, vault
2. D, parallel bars
3. B, floor exercise
4. A, balance beam
5. E, pommel horse

Men's Events: horizontal bar, parallel bars, rings, pommel horse

Women's Events: balance beam, uneven bars

Both: floor exercise, vault, individual all-round, team competition

Sun + Moon = All-Star (page 51)

1. b
2. a
3. c

Five-Day Forecast (page 58)

Monday: 95°F

Tuesday: 100°F

Wednesday: 88°F

Thursday: 77°F

Friday: 79°F

The Metric System (page 59)

1. 33 feet
2. 110 yards
3. 72 miles
4. 121 pounds
5. 46 feet by 5 feet

Challenge: Perimeter = 102 feet, Area = 230 square feet

Adding Oomph (page 60)

Accept reasonable responses.

Which One Doesn't Belong? (page 62)

1. Barcelona
2. boxing
3. Paris
4. yellow
5. golf
6. Texas
7. 1944
8. knife
9. Melbourne
10. sailing

Internet Research Sites

For more information on the Beijing 2008 Olympic Games, visit the following websites:

- *en.beijing2008.cn*
- *www.usolympicteam.com*
- *www.olympic.org*
- *www.wikipedia.com*